Colour

red

yellow

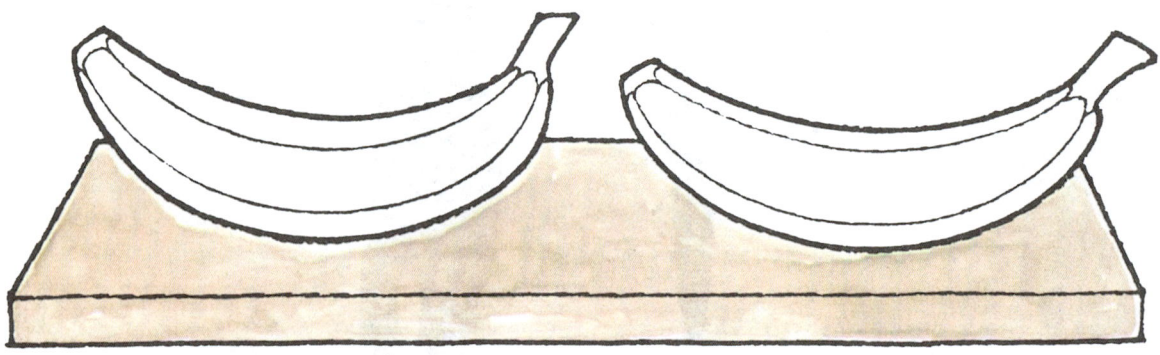

green

Colour

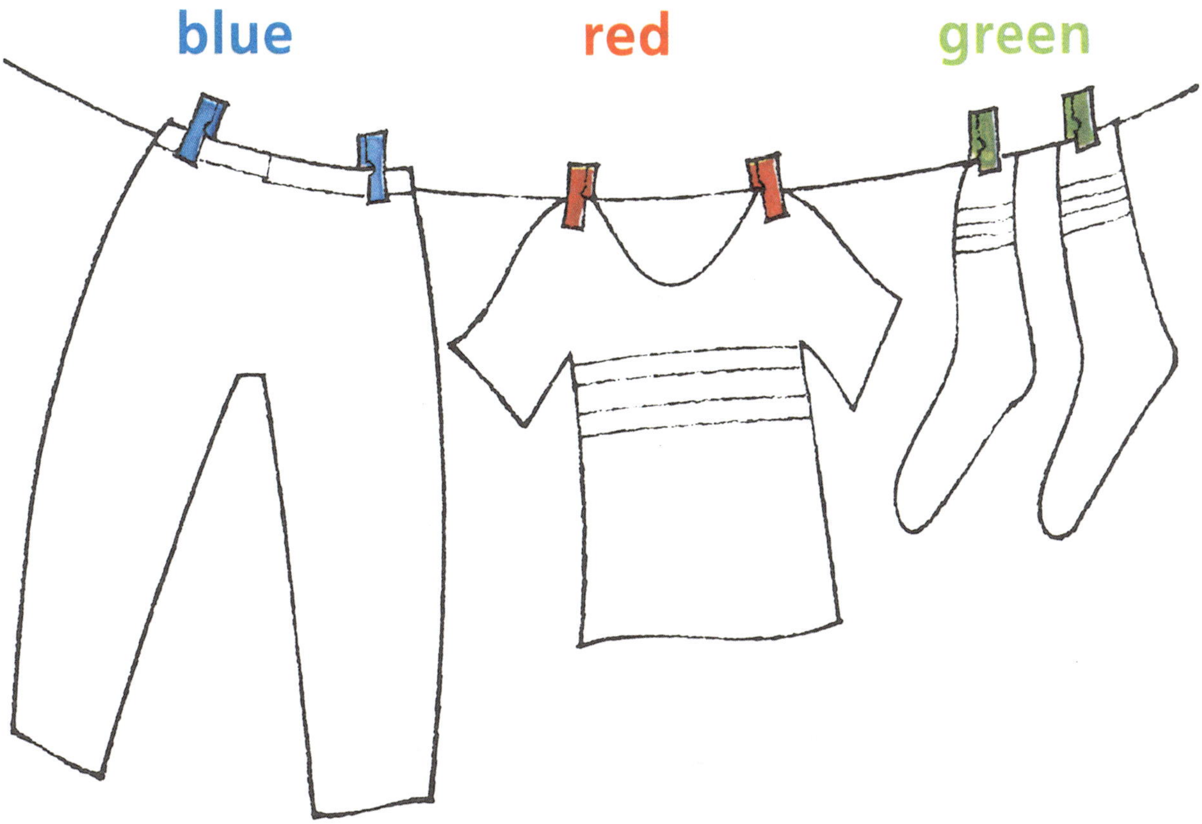

blue red green

yellow green blue

Sorting by colour

Draw sets.

red balloons

blue balloons

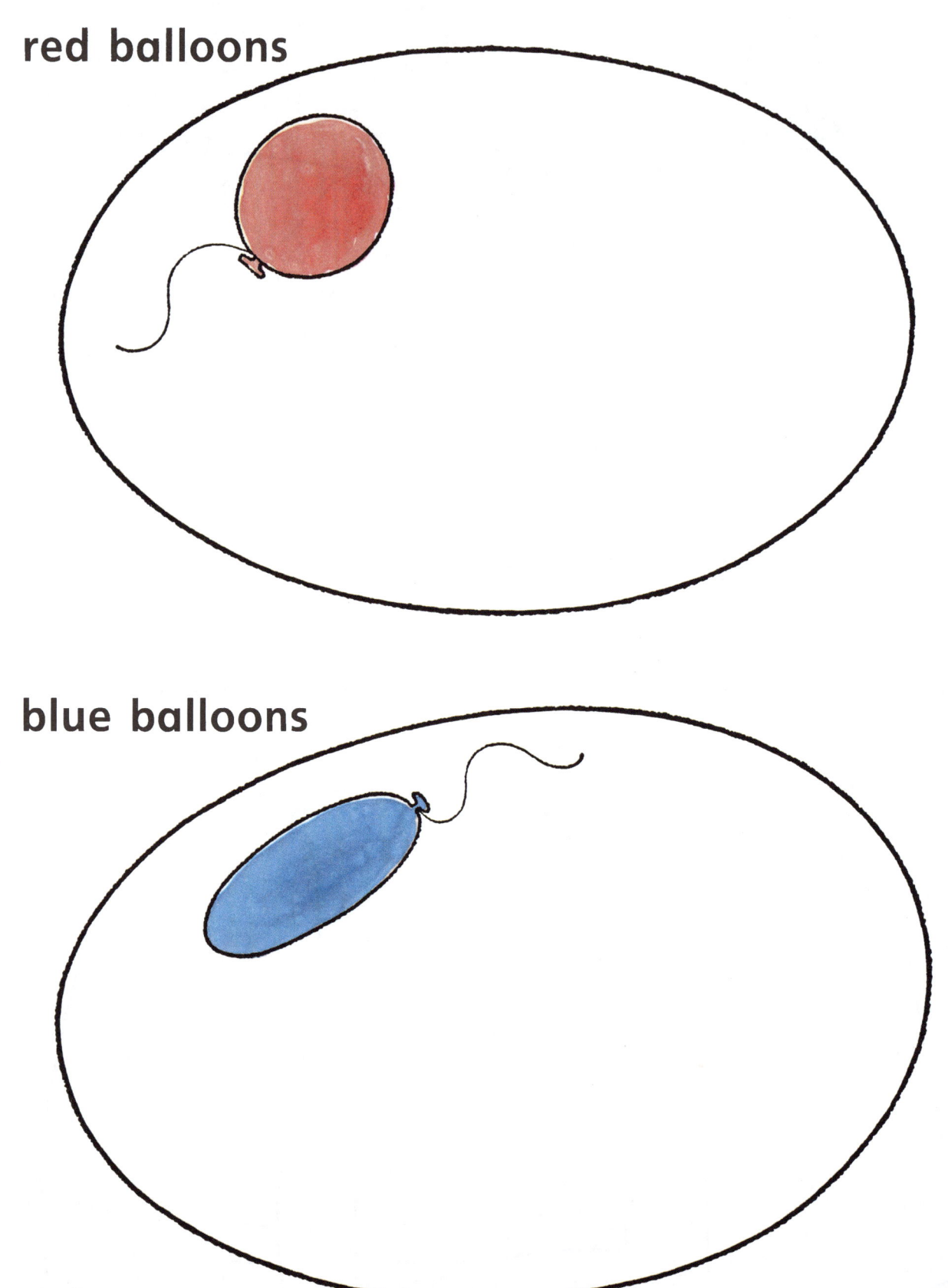

Draw rings to sort.

Colour to sort.

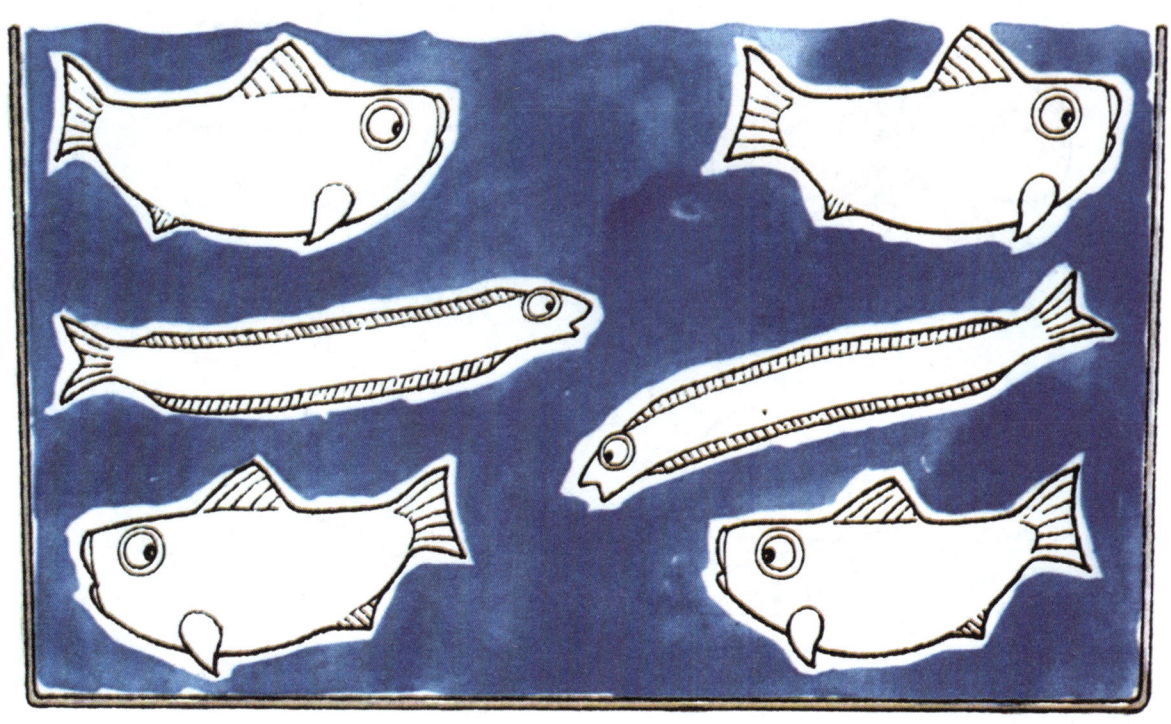

Sorting by size

Colour to sort.

Dogs

Sort into 2 sets.

Sort into 2 other sets.

Match and colour.

Matching pairs

Match

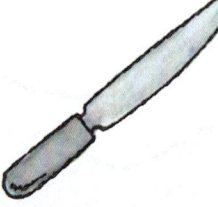
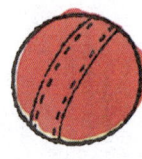

Match

Draw straws.

Draw eggs.

Draw tails.

Match

Which set has more?

Matching

12

Drawing sets with more

Draw more.

lollies

eggs

Colour the beads.

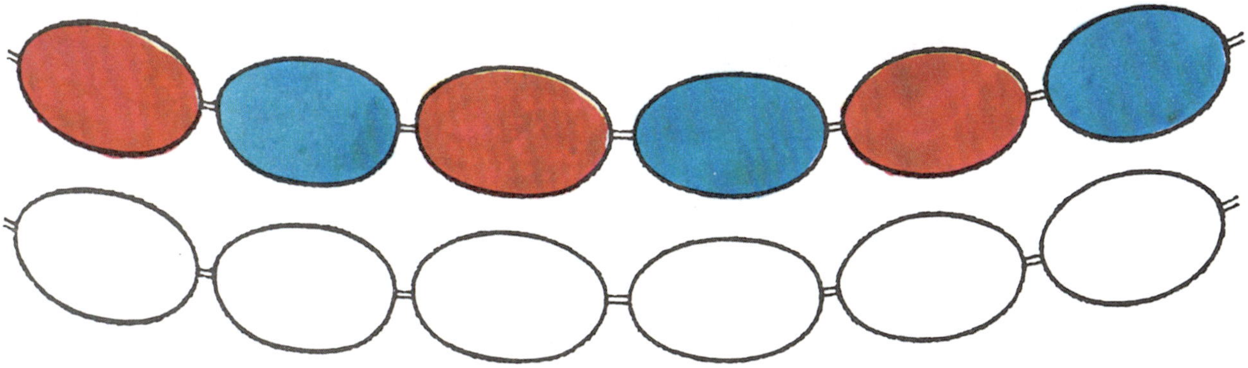

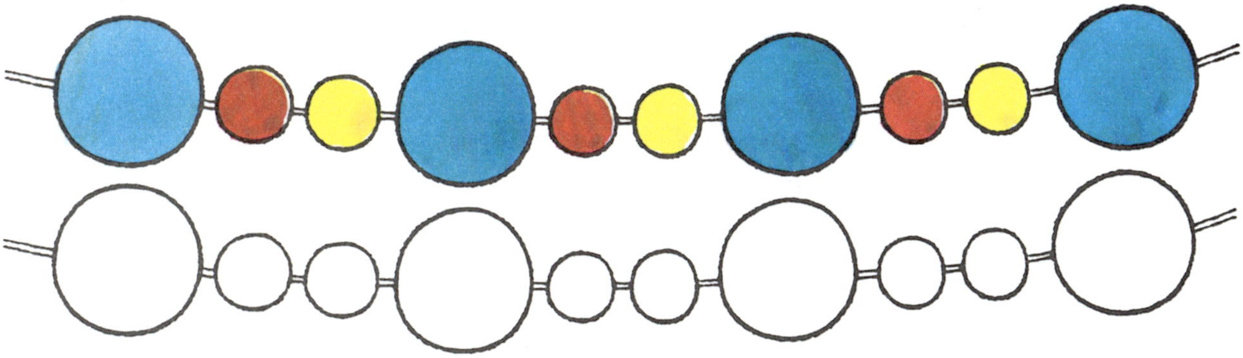

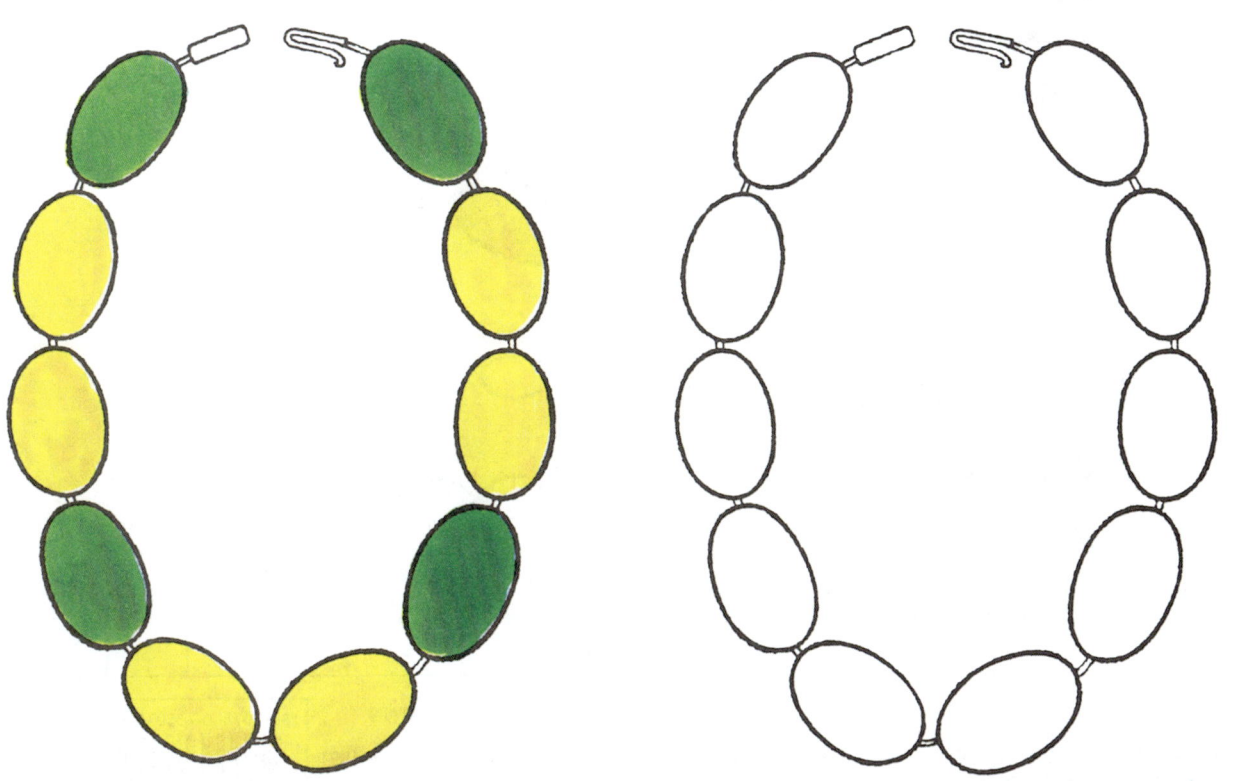

Extension

Continuing patterns — **Problem solving / Extension**

Colour the beads.

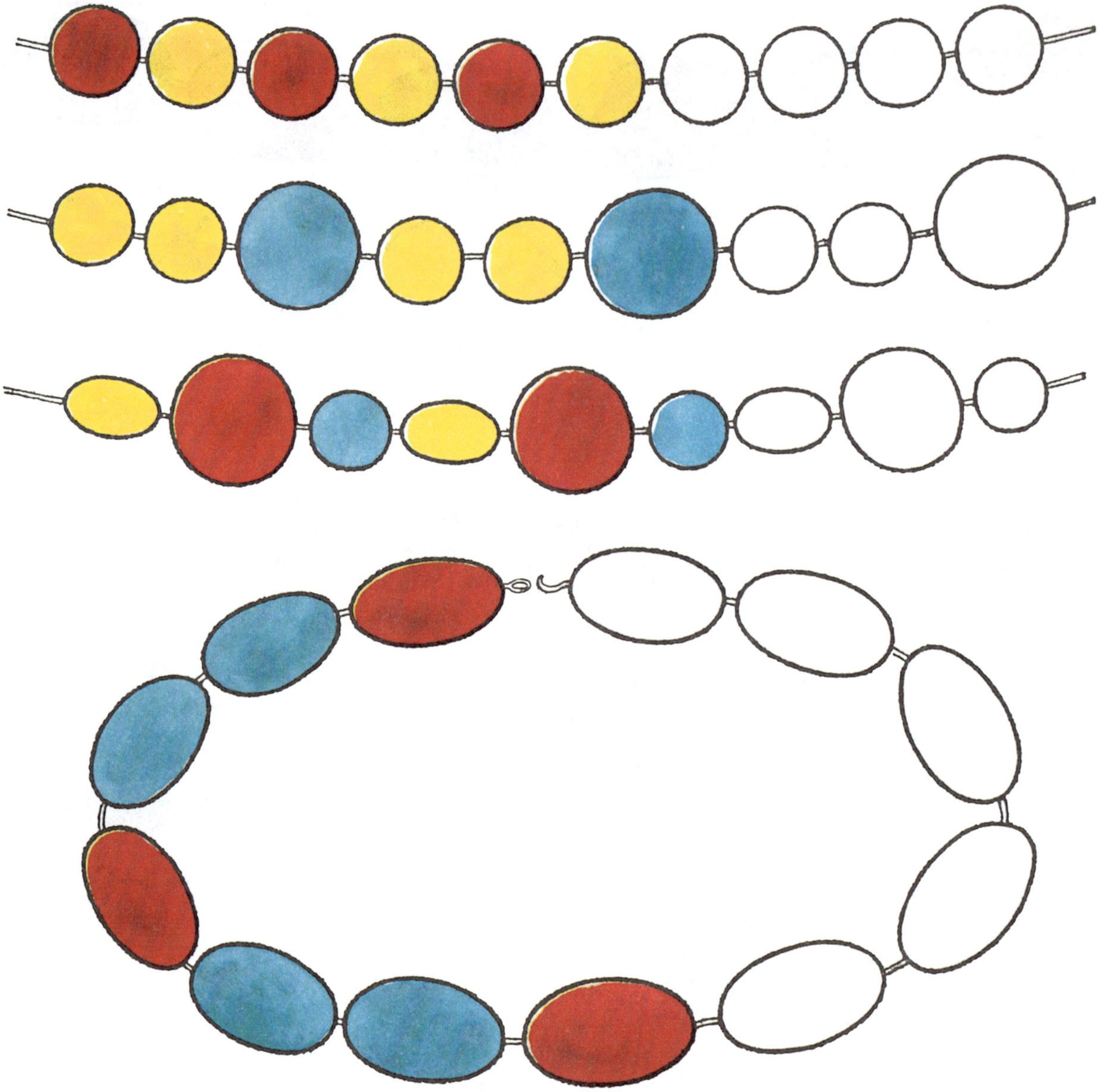

Use beads. Make a pattern.

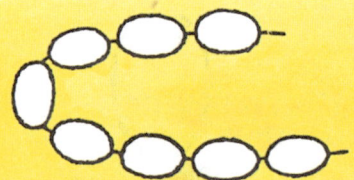

1	2	3	4	5	6	7	8	9	10	11	12	13	14	15